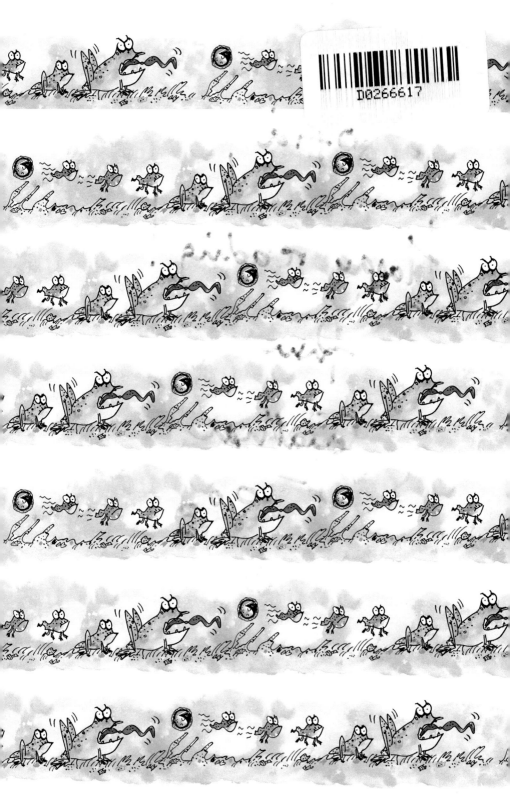

To Sofia,

Happy reading!
from

Jonathan

The EXTRAORDINARY EXPLODING FROG

Written by **JONATHAN STEVENSON**

Illustrated by **MARK BEECH**

YOSHBOSH BOOKS

YOSHBOSH BOOKS

First published in Great Britain in 2016
by YoshBosh Books
001

Visit us on the web at
www.yoshboshbooks.co.uk
yoshboshbooks@gmail.com

Text copyright © Jonathan Stevenson, 2016
Illustrations copyright © Mark Beech, 2016

Jonathan Stevenson and Mark Beech assert the moral right
to be identified as the author and illustrator of this work

Edited by Jane Burnard
Design and art direction by Mandy Norman

A CIP catalogue record for this book is available
from the British Library ISBN: 978-1-5262-0559-9

Printed and bound in Great Britain by
Short Run Press Limited, Exeter, Devon, EX2 7LW

For my wife Sarah and my children,
Emily, James and Sofia
(and Yoshi)

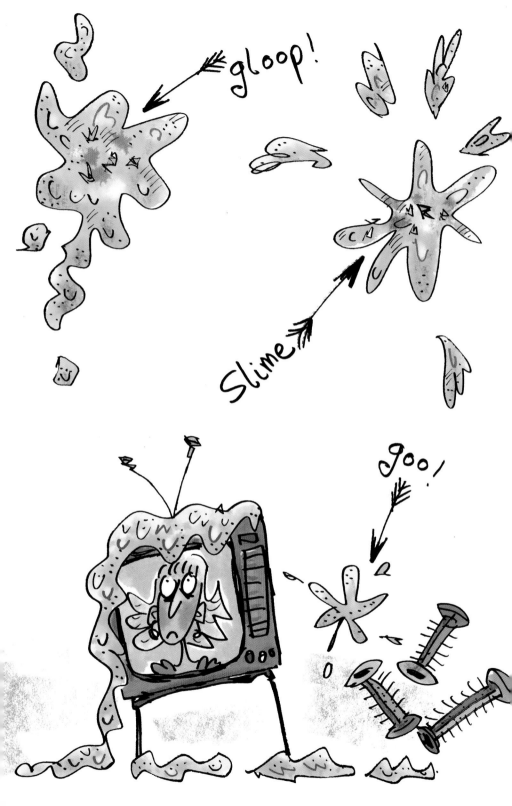

Before we start, may I suggest?

That, my friend, it might be best

To think most carefully before proceeding

Before you decide to go on reading . . .

This tale is not for the faint of heart

(Particularly the **exploding** part . . .)

So if you don't like **slime**

or **gloop**

or **goo**

Please go and find something else to do.

Well, you have been warned – so on we press

(I hope you are not prone to stress)

Let me tell you about the Meeker family

Whose lives turned quite extraordinary.

Milo Meeker was eight years old

And didn't *always* do as he was told:

He liked to play and get really dirty

And stay up later than seven-thirty.

He liked mini-**beasts** and **giant** snails

Tiny **tree frogs** and **enormous** whales ...

Yes, Milo Meeker was an animal lover

But he didn't *always* love his mum and brother ...

His mum was always on his case:
'Wash your hands and wipe your face!'
And she would not take him to the zoo:
'Stinky beasts! And scary too!'

She cleaned all day, grumbled and griped
And chased him round with baby wipes.
'Stop making a mess! Pick up that crumb!'
No, she really wasn't that much fun.

Grime!!!

His brother Ben loved telling tales

'**It's Milo's fault!**' he always wailed.

'He did it! His fault!' Ben would mither

No, little brother Ben was no fun either.

And it was not much better at Milo's school

His headmaster had a thousand rules;

Waiting each day at the school gate

Yelling

'Meeeker!

Why are you ALWAYS late?'

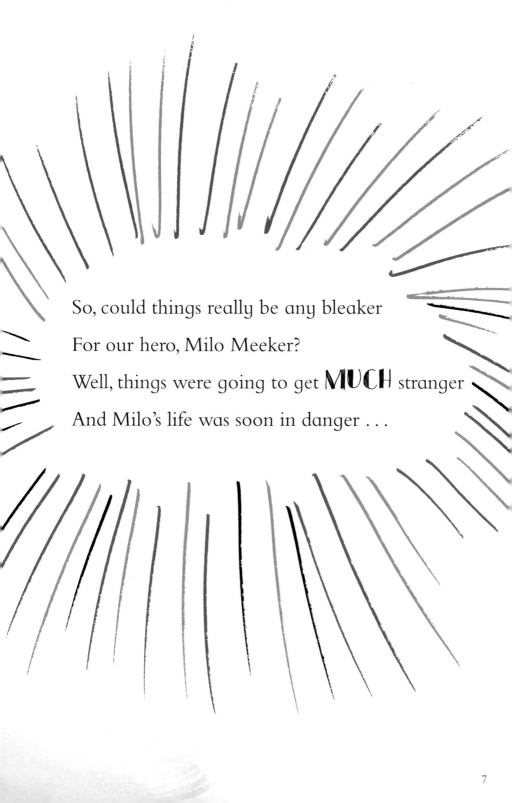

So, could things really be any bleaker

For our hero, Milo Meeker?

Well, things were going to get MUCH stranger

And Milo's life was soon in danger . . .

Still here, dear reader? I thought you'd gone.

It's time to move our story on

And take you to that fateful day

When it all began to go astray . . .

The park was Milo's favourite place

With a lake and ducks and lots of space

And no Mum to fret and fuss about

Or Ben to whine and scream and shout.

So, on that day he was in the park

'Just be back before it's dark,'

His mum had warned before he left,

'And don't get muddy! And don't get wet!'

But Milo hadn't really listened

The sun was shining and the water glistened

He crouched down close to the lake shore

Leaning over, more and more . . .

What are those black things swimming in shoals?

Oh wow! I think that they're tadpoles!

And that's when Milo fell right in

And was quickly soaked through to his skin.

Shivering, he squelched back down his street

Soaking wet from his head to his feet.

With dread he pushed open the front door . . .

And water sloshed on to the floor.

Ben took one look and screamed out loudly,
'It's Milo's fault!' Then stood there, proudly.
From upstairs his mum shrieked down,
'What on earth has he done NOW?'

She came charging quickly down the stairs
With big pink rollers in her hair ...
Ben pointed at his soggy brother;
'What's all that mess?' roared his mother.

'**Eeek!** There's dirty water on the floor!

'Look, in your boots! There's even more!

'That water stinks – it's really smelly!

'Fetch the mop! Take off those wellies!'

'My lovely house – ruined! I could cry!

'No dinner for you! No shepherd's pie!

'I need to finish off my hair;

'I'm going for a lie-down upstairs!'

Back up she stomped and slammed the door

Milo stared down at the floor . . .

Ben skipped off, singing 'What a shame!

'Poor old Milo got the blame!'

But Milo Meeker was all smiles

As TADPOLES were **wriggling** on the tiles.

And more were in his wellies, too:

'Wow! Now I can have a tadpole zoo!'

Quickly, he scooped the tadpoles up
And emptied his wellies, with a cup.
Filling a jar, it was such fun.
'There is *no way* I'm telling Mum!'

He added a plant and some stones
'This should make them feel at home.'
I've got some pets at last! he thought
But what would happen if he got caught?

And so he hid them in his room
'It's OK, they'll grow up quite soon
'And then I'll go and set them free.
'That sounds pretty good to me!'

Milo loved his cool new pets:

'I wonder how big a tadpole gets?

'That one looks bigger than the rest

'And he looks like he's a bit of a pest!'

'He keeps on chasing all the others!

'Maybe *he's* got LOTS of annoying brothers!

'Maybe *he* always gets the blame, like me,

'And maybe that makes *him* really angry!'

So Milo lay there on his bed

Thoughts of tadpoles in his head;

He didn't notice the day pass by

'Who cares about nasty shepherd's pie?'

Bedtime came. If only Milo knew …

That in that jar, that tadpole **grew**

And **grew**

And **grew**

And **grew**

And **grew...**

Much, much bigger than all the others

Bigger than its sisters and its brothers

And when it ran out of things to eat

It looked around for some fresh meat . . .

And so, in the middle of that night,

To satisfy its appetite,

It ate its brothers, one by one

And its sisters, till there were none.

All were gone with one last

'Sluuurrp!'

As it closed its eyes and let out a

burp!

Sound asleep, Milo did not know

That legs began to **grow**

and **grow** ...

Soon it was a tadpole no more

And water spilled on to the floor.

As in the jar a FROG now sat,

Green as grass and OH SO FAT!

The jar moaned and groaned as the frog got fatter

It cracked and then, with a

BANG,

it shattered.

Water gushed out as it broke

And the frog let out a mighty . . .

23

Milo slept quite heavily
So fortunately he didn't see
Fortunately he was unawares
That the frog had hopped off down the stairs.

There it sat on the kitchen mat
Grinning, like a Cheshire cat
Rolling its tongue out and in
Rooting for food in the kitchen bin.

Potato peelings, chicken wings
And lots of other disgusting things
Made the most tremendous feast
For this great big slimy beast.

Upstairs sleeping, Milo dreamed

Of racing cars and big ice creams;

Downstairs, the amphibious kitchen raider

Jammed its head in the refrigerator.

The sun rose slowly in the sky

While the frog finished off Mum's shepherd's pie.

Nothing was left, the cupboards were bare –

Milo slowly awoke upstairs . . .

As he lay there in his bed,

Tadpole thoughts swam in his head:

I wonder if they've grown overnight?

Do tadpoles sleep? I think they might.

Legs out of bed, toes touched down,

Milo's smile turned to a frown . . .

'Errr . . . why is my carpet completely soaked?'

Downstairs, SOMETHING loudly croaked . . .

Milo spun around – 'What was *that*?

'And why is there glass all over the mat?

'There's glass and water everywhere!'

And then

he scrambled

down the

stairs.

He peered nervously round the kitchen door

'Why is there *slime* all over the floor?'

'CROOOOOAK!'

went the frog, and flicked out its tongue

Milo ducked and shouted, 'Mum!'

The floor was soaked with froggy gloop

Mixed in with minestrone soup;

The walls were smeared with jam and mustard,

The ceiling was **dripping** globs of custard.

His mum came downstairs with a clatter
'What's happened now? What's the matter?'
She burst in through the kitchen door
And slid right across the greasy floor . . .

She could not stop, her arms were flapping
The frog sat, mouth open, tongue a-lapping
She screamed out, terror in her eyes:
'It's eaten up my shepherd's piiiiiiiiiiie!'

'**Heeeelp!**' she yelped, but it was no use

As she sped along on froggy juice

Straight towards the open mouth:

'Just look at the state of my lovely house!'

With a terrible '**Sluurrrp**'...

she was gone.

Milo howled, 'What have you done?

'You've eaten her! You ate my mum!

'Nothing's left! Not one crumb!'

33

Things then got even stranger when

In through the door came little Ben

'Milo's fault again!' he squealed

And, with that, his fate was sealed.

The frog took one look and Milo knew

That the frog would gobble Ben up too.

Sure enough, out shot the tongue

And wrapped round Ben, just like his mum.

Milo couldn't help but giggle;

All Ben could do was squirm and wriggle:

'You horrid toad! Let me go!'

'He's **NOT A TOAD**!' snarled Milo.

And then, the very strangest thing.

The frog. It smiled. And winked at him.

Milo's chin nearly hit the floor.

But the frog just squeezed Ben even more.

It flicked him up into the air
Milo, below, could only stare;
Ben cried out 'MILO'S FAULT!'
And then he did a somersault,

And then another, round and round,
Hurtling down towards the ground
The frog sat still and opened wide
And Ben disappeared down deep inside.

Milo was far too shocked to shout

And then once more the tongue shot out –

It wrapped tightly around poor Milo's waist . . .

But was Milo Meeker to this frog's taste?

The frog lifted Milo way up high

And then the two were eye to eye;

Would it eat him? Or let him go?

Turn the page and I'll let you know.

'**BLEK!**' went the frog and released its grip

And its tongue shot back, just like a whip.

Milo knew that he was lucky:

'He must think that I taste YUCKY!'

 Sure enough, the frog just sat

(It really was

enormously fat.)

'I think he's full. Look at his belly!'

The frog just smiled. And ate the telly.

Now Milo was cross as cross can be.

'You've gobbled up my family!

'And now the television too?

'What on earth is wrong with you?'

The frog just stared right back at him

With its lips curled up in a gruesome grin

Sat in the most gigantic pool

Of **slippy**, **slimy**, **froggy** **drool**.

Milo didn't know what to do:

'Maybe I should call the zoo?

'They could catch him with a net

'Or I could keep him, as a pet!'

But before another word was said

The frog hopped high over his head

Out through the door and into the road . . .

The milkman yelled, 'Look! Runaway toad!'

'**HE IS NOT A TOAD!**' Milo replied

The milkman quickly ran off to hide

The postman wailed, 'That frog's gone bananas!

'And a little boy is outside in his pyjamas!'

With that he dropped his sack and fled:

'I shouldn't have got out of bed!

'Call the police! Call the army!

'A frog is going completely barmy!'

A jogger out for her morning jog

Was almost trampled by the frog

And there really was a terrible fuss

When the frog jumped over the Number Ten bus.

People stopped and stared and then

The frog turned right and right again

And Milo chased it, shouting, 'Wait!'

But the frog bounded through his school gate.

'Where are you going? Wait for me!'

And the frog leaped into the assembly

Everyone was gathered in the gym

And EVERYONE stopped and stared at him . . .

The headmaster shouted, 'Out, I say!'

(But this was not his lucky day.)

'Whose frog is this?' the headmaster cried;

'He's m–m–mine, sir,' Milo replied.

Milo stepped in front of his web-footed friend

(Would *he* now come to a sticky end?)

He could see the headmaster was about to yell . . .

'Sir . . . I've b – brought him in for Show and Tell.'

Then the frog sprang up over Milo's head

The headmaster's face went the brightest red:

'Out! Out, I say! Stop! Get back!'

But the frog ate him for its morning snack.

For a second, no one made a sound

Then the kids all cheered and jumped around:

'Our rotten headmaster's being digested!'

(I'm afraid he really was quite detested.)

And then came a rumbling noise, deep and low…

'That giant frog's about to blow!'

Called out the kids in great delight

It really was a terrible sight.

Its eyes grew big, yellow and wide

What on earth was going on inside?

Everyone stopped and stared at the beast –

It couldn't digest its latest feast . . .

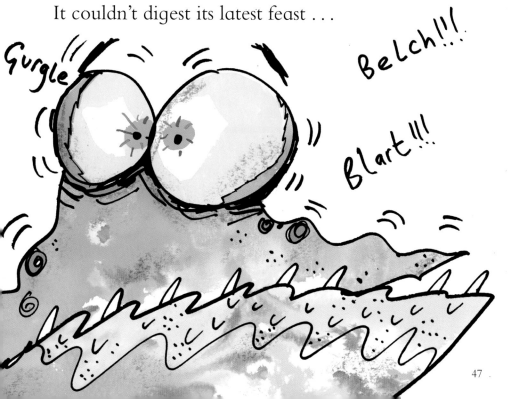

Its belly swelled up more and more

And its tongue lolled out on to the floor

'BUURRP' it went and

'BUURRP' again

'BUURRP,

BUURRP

BUURRP

BUURRP,

and then . . .

Suddenly, with the most enormous

POP!

The frog **exploded** and, with a mighty

PLOP!

It showered the kids with yucky goo . . .

Out came Mum, Ben and the headmaster too.

Yes, they shot out at a tremendous rate

All in a fairly dreadful state

And more than a little traumatised

From spending time in a frog's insides.

Milo's mum moaned in despair:

'I'd only just curled my lovely hair!'

And after (yet another) somersault

Ben lay, whimpering, 'M–M–Milo's . . . f–fault.'

'**Meeeker!**' bellowed the headmaster

'You're to blame for this disaster!

'The walls are covered in froggy drool!

'I'm going to have to close the school!'

The kids all sang out Milo's name

So he didn't mind getting all the blame:

'*Milo Meeker – he's so COOL!*

'*Thanks to him – NO MORE SCHOOL!'*

But Milo didn't jump about
He didn't cheer. He didn't shout.
He couldn't believe his awful luck –
His new pet frog had just blown up.

'I'll never have another pet
'So . . . maybe I'll become a vet!
'Then I'll be with animals every day
'That's not work – to me that's play!'

So now he gets to school on time
(And he helped clean up the froggy slime)
The headmaster is a little less mean
(But has a terrible fear of anything
green . . .)

Things are better at home now too

Mum even takes them to the zoo.

She has less grumbles and less gripes

(But still carries round the baby wipes.)

Ben says 'Milo's fault!' much less

(Even when Milo makes a mess.)

Yes, the perils of that fateful day

Have changed them all in some small way . . .

The newspapers all reported the story

(They like it when a story's gory):

KIDS WATCH DEMON FROG EXPLODE

TEACHERS TELL OF TERRIBLE TOAD

'HE. WASN'T. A. TOAD!'

It makes Milo mad.

He still misses his pet, which makes him sad . . .

'He was better than any

        mouse, rabbit,

                cat or dog . . .

'He was my

EXTRAORDINARY,

EXPLODING,

FROG!'

So, Milo knew the differences between frogs
and toads, but do you?

FROGS have smooth, moist skin
and long, stripy legs and are most
likely to be found in damp places in
the garden.

TOADS have warty skin, beautiful
golden eyes and prefer to crawl
around rather than hop. They
can puff themselves up if they
feel threatened too! Toads can
live in drier habitats than frogs and spend less
time in water. *

★ Neither frogs nor toads eat people or electrical appliances!
Nor have there been any recorded cases of exploding amphibians.

DID YOU SPOT THE FLIES?
There are a few flies buzzing around in the story,
so go back and see if you can find them all (before the frog
does!). If you need help, just turn this page upside down.

There are 6! Pages 1, 3, 8, 23, 31, 55.

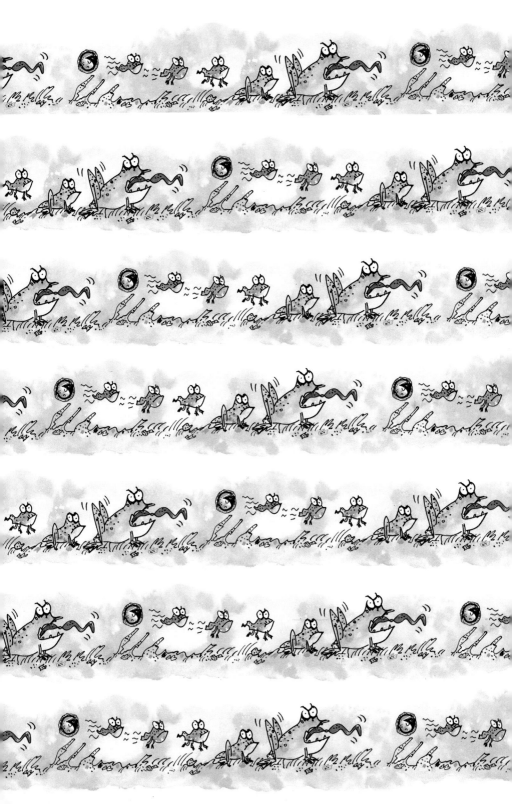